Noah and the Ark

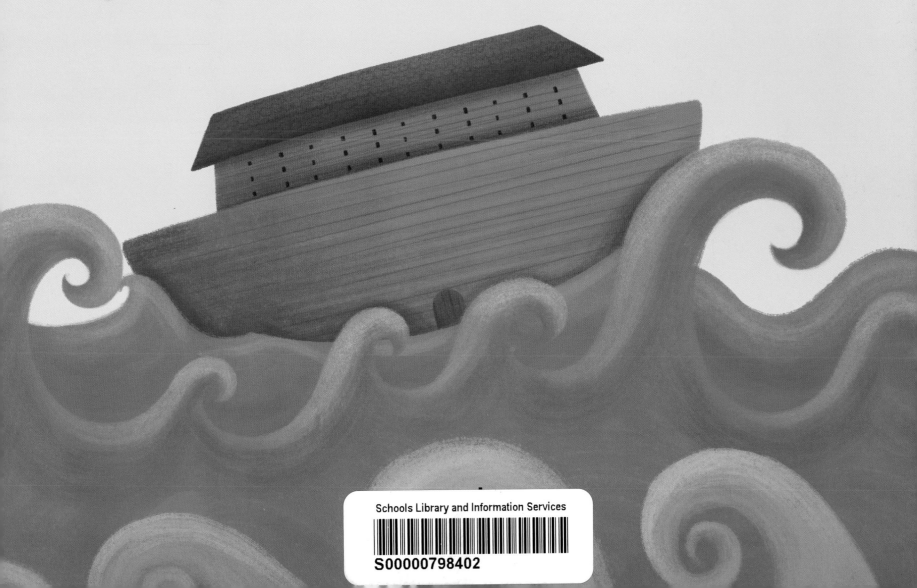

When God first made the world,
it was very beautiful.
Everything was peaceful and
everyone was happy.

But people did not **respect** the world or each other.

This made God **sad.**

People were selfish, cruel and **wicked**.
They were mean to each other, and
fought over everything.
This made God **angry**.

One man above all others was
good, **honest** and hard-working.

His name was Noah.
God **was pleased** with Noah, his wife
and their three sons and wives.

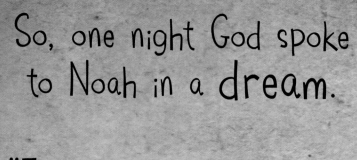

So, one night God spoke
to Noah in a dream.

"I am going to flood the
world and wash it clean
again," God told Noah.

"You will need to build a
huge wooden ark
to save your family and two
of every living creature."

The next day, Noah, his wife,
their sons and their wives began
the **enormous task**
God had given them.

They used the best wood they could find and **slowly** the ark took shape.

"We must give it a roof of reeds and **coat it with tar** to make it water-tight," said Noah.

Eventually the ark was finished. It was 133 metres long, 22 metres wide and 13 metres high.

There were three decks with lots of different rooms for Noah, his family and all the animals.

"Now we must find food for everyone," said Noah.

And while they loaded the ark, Noah's neighbours looked on and laughed.

Next, Noah collected one pair of **every** animal, just as God had asked him to.

The animals walked, hopped, crawled, slithered and were carried **two by two** onto the ark.

Noah's neighbours laughed even louder, but Noah **trusted God.**

One week later, God sent the first storm clouds and it **began to rain.**

Rivers, lakes and oceans quickly swelled. Water flooded the land and the ark **floated away.**

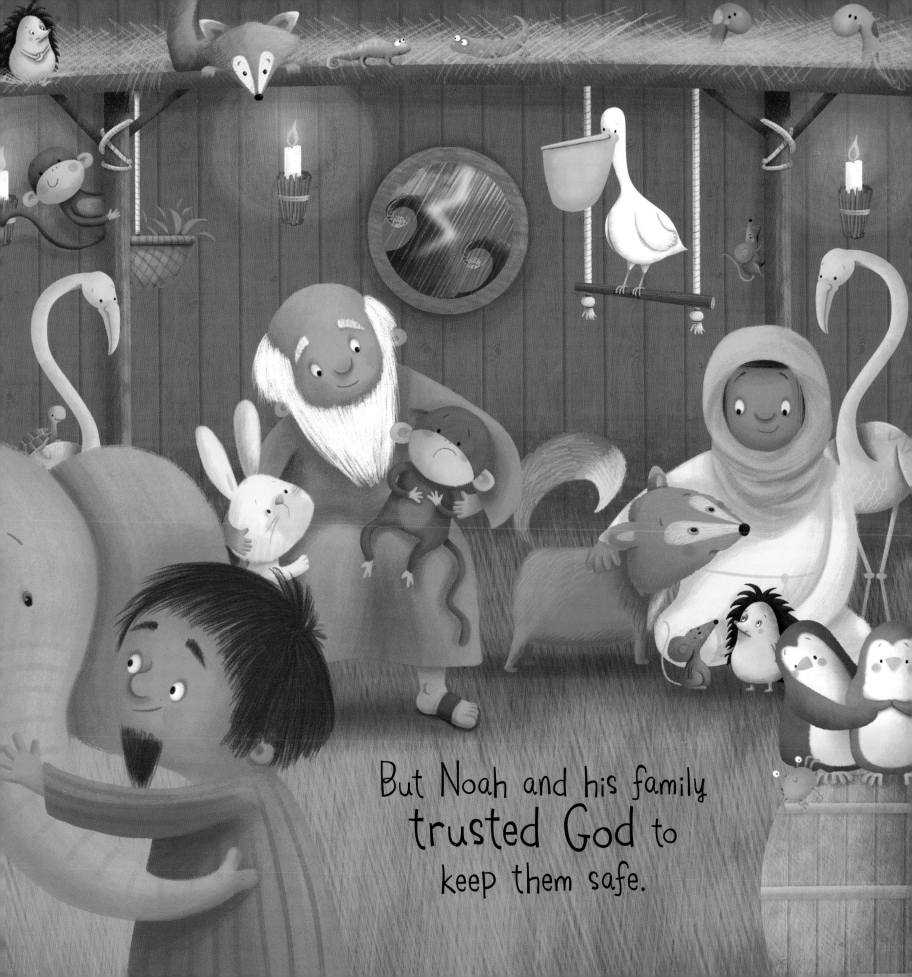

But Noah and his family
trusted God to
keep them safe.

It rained and it rained, and the world was **washed clean** by an enormous flood, as God had wished.

Soon even the **highest mountains** were covered by the water, and still the rain came.

It rained for **forty days and forty nights,** then as quickly as it started, it stopped.

The ark came to rest on
the top of a huge mountain.
"I can't see anything but water,"
said Noah, peeking out.

Then God sent a **wind** to begin drying up the water and the **sun** shone down on the flood.

Noah waited for a week, then he sent out a **raven**.

"If there is **dry land** anywhere, the raven will find it," he said to himself.

But the raven soon came back to the ark.
Noah **waited another week**
and then sent out a dove.

This time the **dove** flew
back with an olive branch.

When Noah **sent the dove out** the next week, it did not return. The dove had found land.

God said to Noah: "The flood is over. It is time for you and your family to leave the ark."

"Go out into the world with the creatures and **begin again,**" said God.

God promised never to flood the world again. As a sign of His vow, He made a **rainbow**...

...to remind everyone of **His promise.**